THIS BOOK BELONGS
TO

TELL ME
ABOUT JESUS

By MARY ALICE JONES
Illustrated by PELAGIE DOANE

RAND M^cNALLY & COMPANY

NEW YORK CHICAGO SAN FRANCISCO

PRINTED IN U.S.A.

CONTENTS

"Once he lived among neighbors in Palestine, very much as we live among our neighbors today. He visited them. He went to church with them. He was friends with them."

"That is the way I would like it," Bobby said. "So we could be friends."

"Those who knew Jesus told others about him," Bobby's mother went on. "And they told others."

"And so he had lots and lots of friends," Bobby added.

His mother nodded her head. "And then, after a while, hi friends wrote about what he did. They remembered to use the very words he used. What they wrote was carefully kept."

"In the Bible?" Bobby asked.

"Yes, dear, right in the Bible. And today we can read what Jesus did and what he said to people long ago."

"How does it help to know what Jesus said to people long ago? I want to know what he says to me right now."

"That is the wonderful part about it, Bobby. When people today read what Jesus did and said long ago, they find the very answers they need to their own questions about how to live today. It seems as though he is talking right to them."

"Tell me about Jesus," Bobby asked his mother. " I want to know what he did."

"I can't tell you all at once, Bobby."

"Then begin to tell me. Let's begin this very minute."

And so Bobby's mother told him about Jesus.

JESUS LOVES CHILDREN

JESUS loved children, Bobby," his mother told him.

"Did he play with them?" Bobby wanted to know.

"I think he did, dear. I know he liked to have them near him."

"Tell me about it," Bobby asked.

"One day he was very busy. A great crowd of people was

around him. Some mothers came to the place where he was. They
had brought their children to see Jesus.

"Some friends of Jesus wanted to send the mothers away.
'Jesus is too busy to see the children,' they said.

"But Jesus heard them. 'Do not send the children away,' he
told his friends. 'I want them to come to see me.'

"And Jesus left the crowd and came to the mothers and the
children. And he talked with the children and made friends with
them. And the children loved him."

"I like to think about that," Bobby said. He was quiet for a moment. "If Jesus lived on our street, I would take Mary to see him. Yes, I would."

Bobby's mother smiled. "I am sure Jesus would be glad to see you and your little sister, dear."

"I will *tell* Mary about him," Bobby decided.

"Mary is not very big yet," his mother reminded him.

"I know she won't understand much," Bobby said. "But I can show her my picture of Jesus and the children. I can say, 'This is Jesus, Mary. Jesus loves children.'"

"I think that will be good, Bobby," his mother told him.

JESUS GOES ABOUT DOING GOOD

DID Jesus live in a nice house like ours?" Bobby wanted to know.

"We do not know exactly what house Jesus lived in, dear," his mother told him.

"I wish somebody had made a picture of it for us."

"Do you, Bobby? So far as we know, nobody made a picture of it."

"Then nobody will ever know about the house Jesus lived in," Bobby said. He sounded so gloomy that his mother laughed.

"Why do you want to know about Jesus' house, Bobby?" she asked. "Is that important?"

"I want him to have a *nice* house, and flowers and pets."

"I think Jesus would have liked a nice house, dear. But after he was grown up, he did not have any house at all."

"Why didn't he?" Bobby asked. "He needed it."

"He probably did need it. But even more than that, he needed to be wherever there were people he could help."

"If he had a nice house, people could come to see him," Bobby said.

"But many of the people who needed him most might not have come, Bobby. They might have thought Jesus had other company. They might have thought he was too busy to be bothered with them."

"The mothers with their children might have thought that."

His mother agreed. "Jesus did not wait for people to come to find him. He went about and found them. And so he could not have a home of his own."

Bobby thought for a while. "But where did Jesus sleep, Mother? He had to have a place to sleep."

"He had many friends, you know. People who loved him. Whenever he was in a town where any of his friends lived, he stayed with his friends. Sometimes he asked a stranger to let him stay in his house."

"If he came to this town, I would give him my room," Bobby said.

"I am sure you would, Bobby."

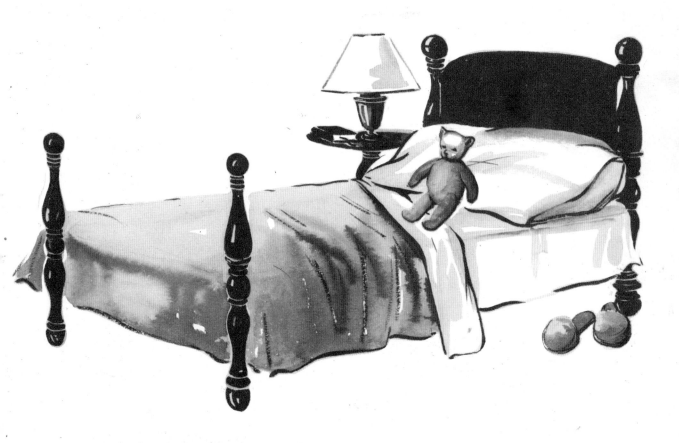

JESUS IS GLAD

BOBBY and his daddy stopped by for Susan and John, and they all went to gather nuts in the woods.

They had a fine time running through the dry leaves that had fallen from the trees. They found nuts underneath the leaves.

On the way home they stopped to watch a squirrel gathering acorns.

That evening Bobby and his mother were talking before Bobby went to bed.

"Did Jesus have a good time?" Bobby asked.

"What are you thinking of, dear?"

"Like today. We had fun. Did Jesus have fun?"

"Jesus liked the out-of-doors, as we do," his mother told him.

"He liked flowers and birds and trees. I think he must have had good walks with his friends, as you did this afternoon."

"I wish he had been with us today," Bobby said. "We had such a good time."

"Jesus liked to watch the children play," his mother went on. "He liked to listen to their laughter. I think he laughed with them."

"Did he ever go to parties?" Bobby wanted to know.

"Yes, the Bible tells about some parties too, dear. People liked to have him because he was a friendly guest."

"I am glad. I like to think about Jesus being happy." And Bobby kissed his mother good-night and went to sleep.

REMEMBERING JESUS' BIRTHDAY

IT WAS Christmas Eve!

Bobby's mother had put Mary to bed. Now she was wrapping up presents. Bobby and his daddy were fixing the last star on the Christmas tree.

"Read about the first Christmas," Bobby asked his daddy.

So his daddy found the place in the Bible and read the story of the first Christmas:

And Joseph went from Nazareth, unto the city of David, which is called Bethlehem, to be taxed with Mary his espoused wife.

And while they were there, she brought forth her first-born son, and wrapped him in swaddling clothes, and laid him in a manger; because there was no room for them in the inn.

And there were in the same country shepherds abiding in the field, keeping watch over their flock by night.

And lo, the angel of the Lord came upon them, and the glory of the Lord shone around about them: and they were sore afraid.

And the angel said unto them, "Fear not: for, behold, I bring you good tidings of great joy, which shall be to all people. For unto you is born this day in the city of David a Savior, which is Christ the Lord. And this shall be a sign unto you; Ye shall find the babe wrapped in swaddling clothes, lying in a manger."

And suddenly there was with the angel a multitude of the heavenly host praising God, and saying, "Glory to God in the highest, and on earth peace, good will toward men."

And it came to pass, as the angels were gone away, the shepherds said one to another, "Let us now go unto Bethlehem, and see this thing which is come to pass, which the Lord hath made known unto us."

And they came with haste, and found Mary, and Joseph, and the babe lying in a manger.

And when they had seen it, they made known abroad the saying which was told them. And all they that heard it wondered.

And the shepherds returned, glorifying and praising God for all the things they had heard and seen, as it was told unto them concerning this child.

And his name was called Jesus.

Selected from Luke 2:4-2

When his daddy had finished reading, Bobby was very quiet for a while. Then he said, "It's Jesus' birthday. But we give other people presents. Why don't we give Jesus presents on his birthday?"

"Why do we give anybody birthday presents, Bobby?" his daddy asked.

"Because we want to be good to people on their birthdays. We want to tell them we love them."

"And we want to tell Jesus we love him on his birthday, too."

"But how can we?" Bobby wanted to know. "What can we give him?"

"One day Jesus was talking with his friends," Bobby's daddy told him. "He was telling them how they could show that they

loved him. 'Whenever you are good to anybody who needs your help,' he said, 'you are showing love to me.'"

Bobby thought about it a moment. "When I am good to Mary, do I show love to you?" he asked his mother.

"That is about the way it is, dear. You see, what Jesus wants most of all is for people to love one another and help one another. And so the very best way to show love to him on his birthday is to show love to other people."

"Then I know what I must do the very first thing on Christmas morning," Bobby said.

"What is that, dear?"

"I must go over to see little Taro and take him a present. They have just come to our town and his daddy and mother haven't had time to plan for Christmas."

"What will you take him, Bobby?"

Bobby thought awhile. "I know what I will take him. I will take him my teddy bear."

His mother hugged him. "I think that is a lovely plan, dear. Daddy and I will send them some of our Christmas dinner, too."

Daddy held out his arms. "Come on, big boy, it is time for bed. Tomorrow is Christmas!"

And so Bobby went off to bed, riding on his daddy's shoulder. As they went through the doorway he asked, "When people show love to each other, is that keeping Christmas the way Jesus would like it?"

"When boys and girls and men and women all over the world show love to one another, then we will be keeping Jesus' birthday indeed," his mother told him.

JESUS GROWS UP

WAS Jesus ever a boy my size?" Bobby asked his mother.

"When Jesus was your age, I imagine he was about your size, dear."

"I knew he was a baby. But I wondered if he grew, like me."

"I think he grew from a baby to a little boy, and then to a big boy, just as you are doing, Bobby," his mother explained.

"And did his mother say every birthday how much he had grown?"

"I am sure his mother watched him grow from year to year. I am sure she talked with her husband, Joseph, about it, just as Daddy and I talk about how much you have grown."

"And did they mark on the tree every birthday to show how tall he was?" Bobby wanted to know.

His mother laughed. "Well, I do not know about that, dear. Maybe marking on the tree to show how tall you are is just something we do in our own family."

"Tell me about Jesus when he was a boy," Bobby asked. "What did he do?"

"Let's put on Mary's cereal first. Then it will be ready when she wakes up from her nap."

So Bobby helped his mother get the cereal ready.

"Now tell me," he said.

"There were some younger children in his home," his mother began. "I am sure he helped his mother take care of them."

"Was he good to them? When he was a boy, I mean?"

"Big children usually like to be good to little children, don't they, son?"

"I like to be good to Mary," Bobby agreed. "But sometimes I forget." He thought awhile. "I like to think of Jesus playing with the little children. What else did he do?"

"Joseph was a carpenter. And I think Jesus learned how to use tools when he was just a little boy. When he was bigger, I am sure he often helped Joseph make things."

"Did he play in the shavings the way I do when Daddy makes things?"

His mother smiled. "All boys do that, don't they, dear?"

"And did he play with other boys?" Bobby asked.

"I think he did. I think he played games that all boys like, Bobby. Running games and music games and 'let's pretend' games. And I think sometimes he climbed up to the top of the hill near his house. I think he watched the people go traveling down the road that led out into the world."

"Was he always good when he was a boy? Did he do what his mother and his daddy told him?"

"What do you think, Bobby? Do you think he was good when he was a boy?"

Bobby thought it over.

"Yes, I do," he decided. "I think he was good. I think the other children liked to play with him. I think his mother and daddy could depend on him."

"I am glad you think he was that kind of boy, Bobby. I think so, too."

JESUS HELPS PEOPLE

JESUS helped all the people who needed him," Bobby's mother told him.

"Tell me about it," Bobby asked.

"One day Jesus was visiting a friend. He had been working hard and he was tired. But some people had heard that Jesus was there. And so they brought sick people to him. Soon there was a crowd about the friend's house.

" 'We need Jesus,' they said. 'He will help our sick people.'

"And so Jesus went out of his friend's house. He touched the hot forehead of a child. He smiled at a worried mother. He went from one to another of the sick and tired and worried people. He helped them all.

"The sun went down. It was dark. Jesus had had no supper.

[33]

Still the people came. Jesus did not leave them. He ___ ved until he had helped the last one."

Bobby listened. "He must have been hungry," he said.

"I am sure he was tired and hungry, Bobby."

"Why didn't he ask the people to wait until after supper?"

"Would it have been good if he had? If he had asked the sick children to wait?"

"No, that would not have been good," Bobby agreed. "Their mothers wanted to get them home."

"Jesus understood about that, Bobby. He thought it was *important* to help people who needed him. He *wanted* to help them. And so he did not mind being hungry and tired."

Bobby looked at his mother. He was remembering.

"You didn't eat any dinner the day Susan's mother was so sick. Daddy told me you stayed right there helping. Did you think about Jesus helping people?"

"Yes, I did, dear."

"And is that why you thought about sending Susan and her daddy their supper that night?" Bobby asked.

"They needed it, Bobby. Jesus showed us that it is right to help people who need us."

"Is that the way Jesus helps us? By showing us what to do?"

"Yes, Bobby, that is one of the important ways Jesus helps us."

JESUS IS BRAVE

BOBBY and his daddy were walking along a country road. They saw a big bull just on the other side of the fence. Bobby was glad that his daddy was with him.

"He is a pretty unfriendly looking animal," his daddy said. "But I do not think he can get out of his field."

Bobby was quiet as they started back home.

"Daddy," he said after a while, "was I afraid of the bull?"

His daddy laughed. "Well, Bobby, you did not look as if you *liked* him very much."

"I would have been afraid if you had not been there."

"That is one of the reasons for having daddies, son. To help children until they learn how to take care of themselves."

"I do not like to be afraid," Bobby said.

"Nobody does, Bobby, but most of us are afraid sometimes."

"Even grown people?"

"Even grown people, Bobby. Most grown people have learned not to be afraid of the things children do not like. But they worry about many things, and that is something like being afraid."

"Was Jesus afraid?" Bobby wanted to know.

"I think Jesus was the most unafraid person who ever lived."

"Tell me about when he was brave, Daddy," Bobby asked.

"There were many, many times when he was brave, Bobby. I will tell you about one time." He thought a moment.

"One time Jesus and some friends were in a garden late at night. Some men who wanted to hurt Jesus came to the garden.

They had big sticks. The friends of Jesus were all afraid. They ran away. But Jesus stood quietly until the men came near him. 'Are you looking for me?' he asked. 'Here I am.'"

"Did God take care of him?" Bobby asked. "So he didn't get hurt?"

"He did get hurt, son. But God helped him to be brave. God helped him not to be afraid of being hurt."

Bobby thought awhile. "I want to be brave," he decided. "But I don't want to get hurt."

"I do not want you to get hurt, either, Bobby. And I will try to keep you from getting hurt. But sometimes it is better to be hurt than it is to run away."

"Like Jesus?" Bobby asked.

"Jesus knew that it is sometimes more important to be brave than it is to be safe," his daddy told him.

Bobby thought it over. He nodded his head slowly. Then he jumped up. "We must get home to our supper," he said.

"That we must," his daddy agreed. "Or Mother will be thinking I have lost you."

"I'll race you to the bridge," Bobby called. And away they ran.

JESUS HELPS PEOPLE TO BE GOOD

WAS Jesus good to everybody?" Bobby asked his mother.

"I am sure Jesus was always kind, dear. What are you thinking about especially?"

"About Henry."

His mother thought a moment. "Henry is not a pleasant boy to play with, is he, Bobby?"

"He's bad, that's what he is. He hits people and he kicks dogs."

"Hitting people and kicking dogs are bad," his mother agreed.

"Would Jesus be good to him?" Bobby asked.

"Let's think about it a little while, Bobby. I wonder what makes Henry hit people and kick dogs."

"I don't know," Bobby said. "How can I know?"

"You see, dear, that is one of the ways in which Jesus was so much wiser than we are. He always thought about the person. And often he found that the person who did bad things really did not like doing them."

"Then why did he?" Bobby wanted to know.

"Let me tell you about a man Jesus met. His name was Zacchaeus. Zacchaeus' work was to collect money. But he cheated his neighbors. He took more money than was fair. That was bad.

Zacchaeus had no friends. Everybody hated the work he did. Everybody hated him for cheating.

"Jesus thought about Zacchaeus. He found out something about him that other people did not know. He found out that Zacchaeus was lonely. And so Jesus became his friend. He went to his house and ate dinner with him. He talked with him.

"And Zacchaeus became sorry for the cheating he had done. He promised to give back all the money he had taken unfairly."

"Was he sorry about it because Jesus was his friend?" Bobby asked.

"I am sure that having Jesus as a friend made the man sorry about cheating," his mother answered.

"Jesus was good to him," Bobby decided. He thought awhile. "Do you think Henry is lonesome? Nobody will play with him."

"Maybe he is, Bobby. Suppose you ask him to play in our yard this afternoon. Then you and I can try being friends with him. Maybe I can make some cookies."

"Goody! I'll ask him right now."

So Bobby and his mother played with Henry in their yard. They made a snowman. Then they went into the house. And they ate

cookies. And Bobby's mother told them some stories. And Henry did not hit anybody and he did not kick Bobby's dog.

That evening Bobby and his mother talked it over.

"I am glad Jesus was good to the man who cheated. I think he was right," Bobby said.

"I think so, too, dear. And I think you and I were right about Henry. He is lonesome. I think he can learn to play without hitting and kicking."

"Let's be friends with him," Bobby said.

SOME PEOPLE WILL NOT LISTEN

DID Jesus make everybody good?" Bobby asked.

"Tell me what you are thinking about, dear," his mother suggested to him.

"Like the man who cheated," Bobby said. "Jesus made him good. Did he make everybody good?"

"We do not always understand how Jesus helps people, Bobby. But I think not all the people who met Jesus became good."

"Why didn't they? I should think they would."

"One reason was that Jesus wanted people to be *really* good. He wanted people to think of others as well as of themselves. He wanted them to love God more than having their own way."

"Is that why Jesus could not make them all good? Because they wanted to have their own way?"

"That is one of the important reasons. You see, when a person is thinking so hard of what *he* wants to do, he just does not want to listen to Jesus." Bobby nodded his head.

His mother went on. "There was a young man who came to see Jesus one day. He came to talk with Jesus about being good. 'What shall I do?' he asked. Jesus looked at the young man. He could tell that he did not cheat or lie. He knew that he went to church. And Jesus liked him. He wanted to be friends with him.

"Now the young man had a great deal of money. And he thought about his money more than he thought about people. It made him selfish. And so Jesus said, 'There is just one thing that is keeping you from being good. You think too much about your money. Give it to the people who need it. Then come with me to help people.'

"But the young man did not want to give his money to others. He wanted to keep it for himself. And so he went away. He did not listen to Jesus any more."

"Did he go away and leave Jesus?" Bobby asked. "When Jesus wanted to be his friend?"

"I should think he would be ashamed of himself," Bobby said.

"Do you, dear?"

Bobby was quiet for a while.

"I should be ashamed, too," he decided. "Sometimes I want my own way, too. Sometimes I do not want to hear anything else."

JESUS AND THE FLOWERS

BOBBY and his mother were looking at their garden. They wanted to see if there were any new blossoms.

"Isn't it good to know that spring has come again, Bobby? Isn't it good to see the flowers and the vegetables and the trees coming alive again?"

Bobby stooped down and touched the soft petals of a flower.

"Did Jesus like flowers?" Bobby asked. "Did he like to watch them grow the way we do?"

"Jesus did like flowers, Bobby. He talked about them. He told his friends that the flowers helped them know about God's love."

"Tell me about it," Bobby asked.

"Jesus and his friends were walking through the fields. There were flowers growing all around them. Jesus stopped to enjoy the flowers. 'Look at the flowers,' he said to his friends. 'See how they grow. They do not worry about how they will be cared for, but God takes care of them. He gives them clothes more beautiful than kings can wear. Why do you not trust God? See how he takes care of the flowers! Will he not take care of you also?' "

"Did his friends like to hear Jesus talk about the flowers and God?"

"I think they did, Bobby. I think they remembered what he said. I think when they saw the lovely flowers growing in the fields, they thought of what Jesus said: 'See how God takes care of the flowers! Will he not take care of you also?' "

JESUS AND UNFRIENDLY PEOPLE

ONE DAY Bobby came in looking hot and angry.

"John won't let me play with his scooter," he told his mother. "I am going to *break* his old scooter. That's what I am going to do!"

"I can think of something for you to do first, Bobby," his mother said. "You can drink a glass of this good lemonade I made to have ready when Daddy gets home."

So Bobby sat down on a stool and his mother gave him a glass of lemonade.

He drank it slowly. He felt cooler. He did not feel so angry.

"Why did I get so mad about the scooter?" he asked his mother.

His mother laughed. "I was wondering about that myself, dear. You do not usually care so much about riding a scooter."

"But John should have let me ride when I asked him."

"Probably he should," his mother agreed.

Bobby finished his lemonade. He took his glass to the kitchen sink. Then he came back and sat down on his stool again.

"Did Jesus get angry with people?" Bobby asked.

"Not in the way you are thinking of, dear. He did not get angry with people who treated him unkindly."

"Not ever?"

"I am sure he did not, Bobby. You see, he just was not the sort of person who thought first about how other people treated him. He thought first about the best way to treat other people."

"What did he do when people were bad to him?"

"I will tell you what he did once," his mother said. "Jesus and some friends were going to take a trip to the city of Jerusalem. They were going to walk. It was a long trip. They would have to find a place on the way to stay all night. Some young men who were with Jesus and his friends went on ahead to a town to find a place to stay.

"When Jesus and his friends came near the town, the young men met them. 'The people in the town will not let us stay here,' they told Jesus. 'The people say they do not like Jerusalem. They will not let anybody stay here who is going to Jerusalem.'

"The friends of Jesus were very angry. 'It is wicked of the people not to give us a place to stay,' they said. 'They are unfriendly to strangers. They are unkind to Jesus. This town should be burned down. Let us ask God to send fire to burn this town.'

"Jesus shook his head. He spoke quietly to his angry friends. 'Would burning down their town make the people feel friendly

toward us?' he asked. 'Come, we will find a place to stay in some other town.' "

Bobby thought awhile. "Those friends were like me," he said. "They were mad. They wanted to hurt people."

He thought some more. "I think Jesus was right," he decided. "Breaking scooters and burning down towns are not good ways to make people feel friendly."

His mother looked at Bobby and smiled.

Then Bobby laughed. "I know what I will do. I will take John some lemonade. Won't that surprise him?"

And it did!

JESUS TRUSTS GOD

DIDN'T Jesus ever get tired of being good?" Bobby asked his mother one day.

"Do you get tired of being good, Bobby?"

"Yes, I do," Bobby said. "Sometimes I want to be bad."

His mother smiled. "I know how you feel, dear. Most people feel that way sometime."

"Did Jesus?" Bobby wanted to know.

"I think that is one of the ways Jesus was different from us, Bobby," his mother told him. "We sometimes want our own way even if it makes other people and ourselves unhappy."

"Didn't Jesus ever want his own way?"

"Jesus trusted God, Bobby. He knew that God's plan was the best plan. He did not do God's way just because he *had* to do it. He did not do it even because he knew it was right. He did it because he loved God and trusted God. And so he *wanted* to do God's way."

Bobby looked out of the window awhile, thinking it over. Just then Mary woke up and called. Bobby went into her room. She held out her hands, and he pulled her up.

"Jesus *liked* being good, Mary," Bobby told his little sister. "He wanted to do God's way. Did you know that?"

Mary did not understand. But she could tell that Bobby was going to play with her. So she laughed happily.

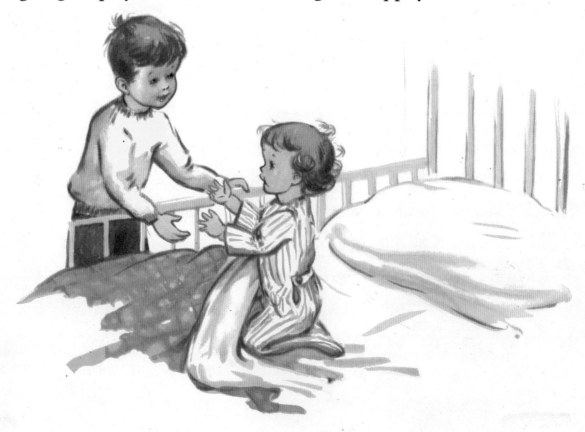

JESUS PRAYS TO GOD

DID God always tell Jesus what to do?" Bobby asked.

"I think he did, Bobby," his mother told him.

"Why doesn't he always tell me?" Bobby wanted to know. "Did he love Jesus more?"

"I do not think that is it, dear. God loves you, too."

"But he always told Jesus and he doesn't always tell me."

"Maybe the difference is somewhere else," his mother suggested. "You see, Jesus always talked things over with God."

"I say my prayers every day," Bobby said.

"I know you do, dear. But I think Jesus did more than say his prayers every day."

"What did he do?"

"One time Jesus was going to choose some helpers. It was very important that he choose the right men. And so he went away from all his friends. He found a quiet place on a mountainside. He stayed there all night, talking with God."

"Did God help him choose the right helpers?"

"I am sure he did, Bobby."

"How did he? How did God tell him?"

"We do not know just how God told him, dear. But we do know one thing about it: Jesus listened. He did not just tell God what he wanted. He listened for God to tell him what to do."

"If I listen, will God tell me, too?" Bobby asked.

"I think Jesus knew how to listen to God better than we do, Bobby. But I know that the more we listen, the more God can help us to know what to do."

JESUS ASKS GOD
TO HELP UNFRIENDLY PEOPLE

WHY didn't everybody love Jesus?" Bobby asked his mother. "He was good."

"One reason, I think, was because Jesus showed them that God wanted them to be good, too. He showed them that God wanted them to love everybody and help everybody."

"And they didn't want to?" Bobby asked.

"They wanted to love and help their own friends, but they did not want to love and help other people," his mother explained.

"Did they think Jesus was wrong about the other people?"

"Yes, they did, dear. And some people thought he was wrong about God, too. They thought he was wrong because he showed them that God loved *everybody*. He showed them that everybody

was important to God. He showed them that God did not have favorites among his children.''

''But that was *right*.''

''Some of the people wanted to feel that God loved them more than he loved other people. They wanted to feel that they were more important to God than other people were.''

''Didn't Jesus tell them that God couldn't have favorites?''

''He showed them, Bobby. But they did not want to understand. They did not want to change.''

''I think he should have let them alone. He should have helped the people who wanted him and let the other people alone.''

"But they did not let Jesus alone, Bobby. You see, they were important people. They thought that *they* were the only ones who should tell the people what to do. They thought Jesus was taking their place. That made them angry. They wanted to stop him."

"Did they stop him?" Bobby asked.

"For a little while they did, dear."

"How could they stop him?"

"They hurt him, Bobby. Soldiers took him away from his friends. Unfriendly people struck him."

"I don't like for people to hurt Jesus," Bobby said. "God should have made them stop. He should have punished them."

"Should he, Bobby? That isn't the way Jesus felt about it. He asked God to help the people."

"When they were hurting him?"

"When they were hurting him terribly. He asked God to forgive them," his mother told him.

"He didn't want God to hurt the bad people who hurt him?"

"No, dear. Jesus wanted God to *help* the bad people. He wanted God to help them be good. That was what was important to Jesus."

"Why was it?"

"Jesus knew that the only way people could be happy was by doing what God wanted them to do. And he wanted people to be happy and good. You see, Bobby, Jesus *loved* people."

Bobby thought awhile. Then he said, "He must have loved them a *lot!*"

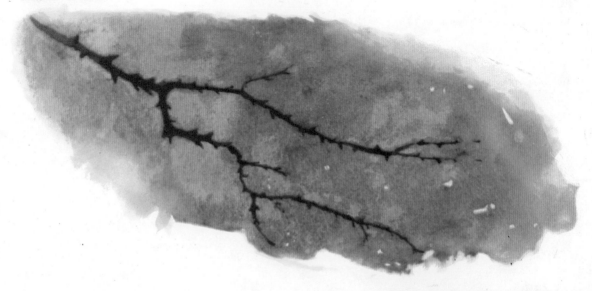

HONORING JESUS AT EASTER

BOBBY opened the door of his church. The sun was shining through the picture window. There were flowers everywhere. And the organ was playing lovely music. Bobby stood very still.

Some bells began to ring, high up in the church tower. Bobby listened. Then it grew quiet again. He closed the door softly. It was time for Sunday School, and he went to the children's room. But he kept thinking about the church and all the flowers.

That afternoon Bobby told his mother about seeing the church and the flowers.

"I am glad you went in, dear," his mother told him. "I think the flowers and the music were more beautiful today than on any Easter that I can remember."

"Why do we have all the flowers and music on Easter?"

"Easter is a happy day, Bobby," his mother told him. "We bring the loveliest flowers to church and sing the most joyous songs. The people who love Jesus want to show how glad they are on Easter."

"Why are they glad on Easter?"

"You remember, dear, that some people did not love Jesus. They wanted to stop him from helping people."

"They hurt him," Bobby remembered.

"Yes, dear. They thought they had stopped him. They thought he was dead forever."

"But Jesus could not be dead," Bobby said.

"That is just what Easter tells us, Bobby. It reminds us that the unfriendly people did not stop him. Jesus was doing what God planned for him to do. He was showing people that God loved them. He was showing them how they could live as God wanted them to live. And so nothing in all the world could stop him."

"What happened on Easter?" Bobby asked.

"On Easter, Jesus came back to his friends. He showed them he would always be with them. I will read it from our Bible":

*A*s it began to dawn toward the first day of the week, came Mary Magdalene and the other Mary to see the sepulcher. And the angel of the Lord descended from heaven, and came and rolled back the stone from the door, and sat upon it. And the angel said unto the women, "Fear not ye: for I know that ye seek Jesus. He is not here: for he is risen, as he said. Go quickly and tell his disciples that he is risen from the dead; and, behold, he goeth before you into Galilee; there shall ye see him."

And they departed quickly from the sepulcher with fear and great joy; and did run to bring his disciples word.

And as they went to tell his disciples, behold, Jesus met them. Then Jesus said unto them, "Be not afraid: go tell my brethren that they go into Galilee, and there shall they see me."

Then the eleven disciples went away into Galilee, into a mountain where Jesus had appointed them.

And when they saw him, they worshiped him.

And Jesus came and spake unto them, saying, "All power is given unto me in heaven and in earth. Go ye therefore, and teach all nations: and lo, I am with you alway, even unto the end of the world."

Selected from Matthew 28:1-20

Bobby looked at the Easter lily on the table. He was thinking of all his mother had told him about Jesus. After a moment he sat down beside her.

"I am glad Jesus came back to his friends," he said. "I am glad he went on helping them. I think God planned it so Jesus would always help people."

"I am sure he did, Bobby," his mother agreed.